Little Golden Books

Little Golden Books

Little Golden Books

Little Golden Books

Little Golden Books

THE LITTLE
GOLDEN BOOK
OF
HYMNS

COLLECTED BY
ELSA JANE WERNER
ILLUSTRATED BY
CORINNE MALVERN

SIMON AND SCHUSTER · NEW YORK

THE LITTLE GOLDEN BOOKS ARE PREPARED UNDER THE SUPERVISION OF

MARY REED, Ph.D.

FORMERLY OF TEACHERS COLLEGE, COLUMBIA UNIVERSITY

Acknowledgments

The publishers wish to thank the following publishers and copy-right owners for permission to use hymns in this book: Harper and Brothers for "Flowers Below and Stars Above." Hope Publishing Co. for "I'll Be a Sunbeam," copyright 1928 by Eliza J. Excell, renewal, Hope Publishing Co., owner. Louise M. Oglevee for "Downy Little Snowflakes" from *The Child's First Songs in Religious Education*. The Pilgrim Press for "Sleep, Little Seed" from *Song and Play for Children* by Danielson and Conant, copyright The Pilgrim Press; "All Things Bright and Beautiful," "God Is Love," and "Growing," from *Songs for Little People* by Danielson and Conant, copyright The Pilgrim Press. The Presbyterian Board of Christian Education for "Evening Prayer" and "A Christmas Prayer," copyright Presby-terian Board of Christian Education. Elizabeth McE. Shields for "A Prayer for Help" from *Worship and Conduct Songs*. Standard Publishing Co. for "I Thank You," copyright Standard Publishing Co. Lorenz Publishing Co. for "Joy in Every Heart," copyright Tullar-Meredith Co. Johnie B. Wood for "The Creation" from *Service in Song* published by American Printing Co.

A Prayer for Help

Elizabeth McE. Shields   Claude T. Carr

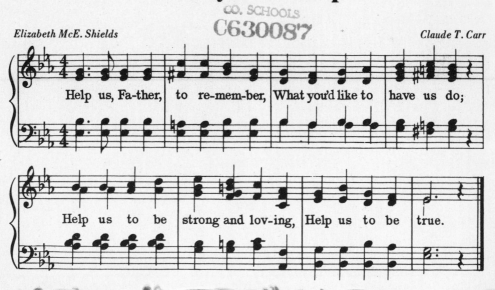

Help us, Fa-ther, to re-mem-ber, What you'd like to have us do;

Help us to be strong and lov-ing, Help us to be true.

The Creation

J. B. W.

Words and Music by Johnie B. Wood

And God said the sun should shine, The
rain should fall, the flow'rs should grow, And God said the
birds should sing, And it was so, was so.

And God said the grass should grow, The
trees bear fruit, the winds should blow, And God said the
streams should flow, And it was so, was so.

Jesus Loves Me

Anna B. Warner

William B. Bradbury

Je - sus loves me! This I know, For the Bi - ble tells me so;

Lit - tle ones to Him be-long, They are weak, but He is strong.

All Things Bright and Beautiful

Cecil Frances Alexander

Adapted from a Danish Folk Song

God Is Love

Frances Weld Danielson

Grace Wilbur Conant

Lis-ten to our Eas-ter song, "God is love," "God is love,"

Now and all the win-ter long, "God is love."

Flow-ers wake that safe were hid-den, Birds come back as they are bid-den,

Chil-dren sing their Eas-ter song, "God is love."

Sleep, Little Seed

Louise M. Oglevee

William G. Oglevee

softly

Sleep, sleep, sleep, lit - tle seed, Sleep through the win - ter long.
Sleep, sleep, sleep, lit - tle seed, Hid - den from sight a - way.

brightly

Wake, wake, wake in the spring, Wake with the blue-bird's song.
Wake, wake, wak - en and grow, Wak - en for Eas - ter Day.

Joy in Every Heart

Mabel J. Rosemon

M. Isabelle Ritter

Songs of re-joic-ing fill the air Ring-ing so sweet and clear.
All Na-ture joins the glo-ry song Ris-ing to heav'n to day,
Come with re-joic-ing, one and all, Come with your pray'r and praise,

Bright-ness and glad-ness ev-'ry-where Tell us that Sum-mer's here.
Each whis-pring breeze that sweeps a-long Bears hap-py notes a-way.
Pray'r that the Fa-ther's bless-ing fall, Praise for these tune-time days.

CHORUS

Joy, joy in ev-'ry heart With new life a-thrill,

Bright, bright the sun-beams glow, Hours with glo-ry fill;

Praise, praise the Lord a-bove, For these gold-en days.

Praise the Lord, O come and praise the Lord, And tell His won-drous ways.

Flowers Below and Stars Above

Bertha Marilda Rhodes

Old Folk Song

Flow'rs be - low and stars a - bove, Ev - er
tell us God is love; Lit - tle chil - dren wake to
say, "Thank you for the glad new day."

Growing

Grace Wilbur Conant

A lit-tle rain and a lit-tle sun, And a lit-tle pearl-y
A lit-tle work and a lit-tle play, And lots of qui-et

dew, And a push-ing up and a reach-ing out, Then
sleep; A__ cheer-ful heart and a sun-ny face, And

leaves and ten-drils all a-bout, And that's the way the
les-sons learned and things in place, Ah! that's the way the

flow-ers grow, Don't you know? Don't you know? And
chil-dren grow, Don't you know? Don't you know? Ah!

I'll Be a Sunbeam

Nellie Talbot

E. O. Excell

Je-sus wants me for a sun-beam, To shine for Him each day;___
Je-sus wants me to be lov-ing, And kind to all I see;___

In ev-'ry way try to please Him, At home, at school at play.___
Show-ing how pleas-ant and hap-py His lit-tle one can be.___

Downy Little Snowflakes

Louise M. Oglevee

William G. Oglevee

Down-y lit-tle snow-flakes Float-ing from a - bove,

Cov-'ring trees and flow - ers, Tell us God is love.

A Christmas Prayer

Calvin W. Laufer

Mildred Adair

Dear God, we thank Thee for the star That shone when Jesus came; O may it shine on us to-night, We ask in Jesus' name.

I Think When I Read That Sweet Story of Old

Mrs. Jemima Luke

Greek Air

I think, when I read that sweet story of old, When
I wish that His hands had been placed on my head. That His

Je-sus was here a-mong men, How he called lit-tle chil-dren as
arm had been thrown a-round me, And that I might have seen His kind

lambs to His fold, I should like to have been with them then.
look when He said, "Let the lit-tle ones come un-to Me."

Evening Prayer

Words adapted by Miriam Drury

Miriam Drury

Now I lay me down to sleep, I

pray Thee, Lord, Thy child to keep: Thy love guard me

through the night, And wake me with the morn-ing light.

I Thank You

Words and Music by Mrs. C. B. Palmer

The — bird - ie says, "I thank you," For the straw to build its nest;— For the bough with leaves all cov - ered, In whose shade it likes to rest.—

The — kit - ty says, "I thank you," For the sau - cer of — warm milk;— And he purrs his thanks quite loud - ly, As you stroke his fur of silk.—

The — cow and horse are thank - ful For a man - ger full — of hay;— If you lis - ten you can hear them, As they say, "Moo, moo, neigh, neigh."—

The — dog - gie, he is thank - ful If you give him scraps of bread,— And his tail wags his, "I thank you," As you stoop to pat his head.—

We — chil - dren, too, are thank - ful For God's lov - ing care and food;— And we'll show by all our ac - tions That we're try - ing to be good.—

E